SPACE
INSTRUCTIONS

1   Carefully remove the viewer from the book along the perforated edge. Gently push each side of the viewer inward. Then push the front of the viewer into place.

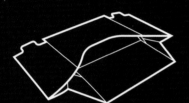 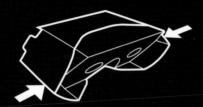 

2   Download PI VR Space, available on the App Store or Google Play. Direct links to the store locations are found at: pilbooks.com/PIVRSpace.

3   Launch the app. If you are asked to calibrate the viewer, go to page 48 and follow the instructions found there. If asked, allow the app to take photos/videos.

4   When the app loads, you will be prompted to scan the QR code found to the right to verify your possession of this book.

5   You will see a double image of a lunar landscape on your phone. Slide your smartphone into the front compartment of the VR viewer. The line between the two images should line up with the seam found on the bottom of the viewer, between the two lenses. If your screen seems blurry, make sure the smartphone is aligned precisely with the center of the viewer. Adjusting the phone left or right a few millimeters can make a big difference. The tilt of the viewer and the phone can also affect how the screen looks to you.

6   Look around to explore! PI VR Space does not require a lever or remote control. You control each interaction with your gaze. When you see a loading circle, keep your gaze focused until it loads fully to access videos, slideshows, and games.

Loading

7   Gaze at the X to close out of video, slideshow, or game screens.

Exit

Get the App!

This book is enhanced by an app that can be downloaded from the App Store or Google Play*. Apps are available to download at no cost. Once you've downloaded the app to your smartphone**, use the QR code found on page 1 of this book to access an immersive, 360° virtual reality environment. Then slide the phone into the VR viewer and you're ready to go.

Compatible Operating Systems

- Android 4.1 (JellyBean) or later

- iOS 8.0 or later

Compatible Phones

The app is designed to work with smartphones with a screen size of up to 6 inches. Removing your device from its case may provide a better fit in the viewer. If your smartphone meets the above operating system requirements and has gyroscope functionality it should support GoogleVR. Publications International, Ltd. has developed and tested this software with the following devices:

- Google Nexus 5, Google Nexus 5X, Google Nexus 6P, Google Pixel

- Apple iPhone 6, Apple iPhone 6S, Apple iPhone 6 Plus, Apple iPhone 6S Plus, Apple iPhone 7, Apple iPhone 7 Plus

- Samsung Galaxy S5, Samsung Galaxy S5 Active, Samsung Galaxy S5 Sport, Samsung Galaxy S6, Samsung Galaxy S6 edge, Samsung Galaxy S6 edge +, Samsung Galaxy Note 4, Samsung Galaxy Note edge, Samsung Galaxy S7, Samsung Galaxy S7 edge, Samsung Galaxy Note 5, Samsung Galaxy S8

Caution

The viewer should not be exposed to moisture or extreme temperatures. The viewer is not water resistant. It is potentially combustible if the lenses are left facing a strong light source.

Cover art from Shutterstock.com

Interior art from Encyclopædia Britannica, Inc., NASA, and Shutterstock.com.

App content from Encyclopædia Britannica, Inc., Filament Games, NASA, and Shutterstock.com

Louis Weber, CEO
Publications International, Ltd.
8140 Lehigh Avenue
Morton Grove, IL 60053

 Publications International, Ltd.

For inquiries email: customer_service@pubint.com

ISBN: 978-1-64030-169-6

Manufactured in China.

8 7 6 5 4 3 2 1

*We reserve the right to terminate the apps.
**Smartphone not included. Standard data rates may apply to download. Once downloaded, the app does not use data or require wifi access.

CONTENTS

INTRODUCTION

The surface of Mars.

Since the beginnings of humankind, people have gazed at the heavens. Before the dawn of history someone noticed that certain celestial bodies moved in orderly and predictable paths, and astronomy—an ancient science—was born. Yet some of science's newest discoveries have been made in this same field, which includes the study of all matter outside Earth's atmosphere.

An artist's rendering shows Voyager 1 entering interstellar space.

IN THIS BOOK

In this book, we'll explore our universe. We'll look at the many ways that humans have explored space. We'll look at the planets of our solar system and the stars we see in the night sky.

USE THE VR VIEWER AND ASSOCIATED APP

Enhance your experience by using the app! Put your smartphone in the VR viewer and you'll be able to explore space in a 3-D environment.

- Scan the night sky to see constellations appear.

- Look towards the Lander to show a video about the Moon landing.

- Once you have watched it, you will see an astronaut whose movements will demonstrate the Moon's gravity.

- Focus your eyes on the Earth to reveal more information about the journey from the Earth to the Moon.

- See a retroreflector, one of the devices left by the Apollo program that uses light to help measure distances between the Earth and the Moon.

- Search for the crater that triggers a game.

Our Sun.

Nebulae

SPACE EXPLORATION

Through space exploration humans have learned a great deal about the planets, stars, and other objects in space. More than 5,000 spacecraft have been launched into space to gather information since 1957. They include spacecraft with humans on board, space probes, and satellites.

YURI GAGARIN
APRIL 12th
1961

THE SPACE RACE

The space age began on October 4, 1957, when the Soviet Union successfully launched the first artificial satellite, Sputnik 1, into orbit around Earth. Less than four years later, on April 12, 1961, Soviet cosmonaut Yury Gagarin became the first human being to travel in space, as he orbited Earth aboard the Vostok 1 spacecraft. Within less than 10 years of Gagarin's voyage, U.S. astronaut Neil Armstrong became the first person to set foot on the Moon, on July 20, 1969.

Learn more about the space race and the Moon landing with the VR viewer!

NOT JUST HUMANS

Unmanned space probes have landed on Earth's Moon and Saturn's moon Titan, on the planets Venus and Mars, and on asteroids. Space probes have also flown past all the planets. Moreover, unmanned spacecraft include sounding rockets and artificial satellites that have been used for scientific raesearch, telecommunications, meteorology, photographic reconnaissance, navigation, and many other applications.

Launch of the Mercury-Redstone 3, the first U.S. manned spaceflight, in May 1961.

THE ROCKET

For flight above Earth's atmosphere a device is needed that carries both its fuel and its oxidizer and that does not depend on the atmosphere for support. That device is the rocket, a reaction engine that operates in accordance with Newton's third law of motion, which states that "for every action there is an equal and opposite reaction." A rocket is propelled by the forward push that results as a reaction to the ejection of exhaust gases from the back of the rocket at extremely high velocities.

In 1972, Apollo 17 was the last of the Moon landings. Astronaut Eugene Cernan was the last person to walk on the Moon.

NASA's Dawn spacecraft was launched in 2007 and is still traveling, gathering information about Ceres and Vesta in the asteroid belt.

HOW DOES SPACE TRAVEL HELP?

A principal reason for the exploration of space is to extend knowledge about Earth, the solar system, and the universe beyond. Artificial satellites have yielded much new information about Earth. Observation posts above Earth's atmosphere permit astronomers to observe radiation that does not penetrate Earth's atmosphere. Spacecraft voyaging far from Earth have gathered new data about the Moon and the planets.

The Antares Rocket test launch in April 2013.

WHAT CAN SATELLITES DO?

- **Meteorological satellites aid in weather forecasting.**

- **Communications satellites multiply international communications channels and make possible the intercontinental transmission of television.**

- **Navigation satellites guide ships.**

- **Military satellites perform vital reconnaissance.**

Little Joe-2, carrying a Mercury spacecraft test vehicle, in November 1959.

ANATOMY OF A LAUNCH

ASSEMBLY AND TESTING

The process of launching a spacecraft starts weeks or months ahead of time with the assembly of the instruments that will perform the experiments or operations of the mission. The components are also tested under conditions that simulate actual flight conditions.

THE LAUNCH VEHICLE

While the spacecraft's instrumentation is being assembled, the components of the launch vehicle are also assembled and tested in a similar process. The final phase of integration is to mate the spacecraft and launcher and exercise them in a countdown demonstration.

THE COUNTDOWN

Prelaunch operations are carried out according to a schedule known as the countdown. This is similar to the checklist followed by an airline pilot, but it is far more complex and involves many more participants.

T-ZERO

Time preceding the launch is known as minus time, or T-minus. Varying with the complexity of the vehicle and its mission, the total length of minus time in a countdown ranges from a few hours to several days. T-time, or T-zero, is the time scheduled for liftoff.

Apollo 10's launch control center in May 1969.

Workers at the Marshall Space Flight Center test the Orion's heat shield in May 2015.

THE
SOLAR SYSTEM

As the Sun rushes through space at a speed of roughly 150 miles (240 kilometers) per second, it takes many smaller objects along with it. These include the planets and dwarf planets; their moons; and small bodies such as asteroids, comets, and meteoroids. The solar system's smallest members are the microscopic particles of dust and the even smaller atoms and molecules of gas of the interplanetary medium. All these objects orbit, or revolve around, the Sun. Together, the Sun and all its smaller companions are known as the solar system. The solar system itself orbits the center of the Milky Way galaxy, completing one revolution about every 225 million years.

Milky Way galaxy.

WHAT IS AN ASTRONOMICAL UNIT?

One astronomical unit (AU) is defined as the average distance between Earth and the Sun: about 93 million miles (150 million kilometers).

SUN

MARS
1.5 AU

EARTH
1 AU

MERCURY
0.4 AU

VENUS
0.7 AU

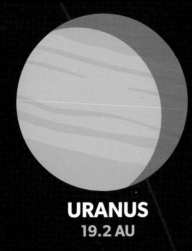

NEPTUNE
30.1 AU

JUPITER
5.2 AU

URANUS
19.2 AU

HOW OLD IS OUR SOLAR SYSTEM?

Astronomers believe the solar system formed some 4.6 billion years ago.

SATURN
9.5 AU

ASTEROID BELT
2 TO 4.5 AU

HOW FAR OUT DOES THE SOLAR SYSTEM EXTEND?

Astronomers do not know exactly how far out the solar system extends. Neptune, the outermost planet, orbits the Sun from about 2.8 billion miles (4.5 billion kilometers) away. Many comets have orbits that take them thousands of times farther out than Neptune. Most comets are thought to originate in the outermost parts of the solar system, the Kuiper belt and the much more distant Oort cloud. The farthest reaches of the Oort cloud extend perhaps to 100,000 AU, or some 9.3 trillion miles (15 trillion kilometers), from the Sun.

Oort cloud comet C/2006 W3.

PLANETS

The relatively large natural bodies that revolve in orbits around the Sun or other stars are called planets. The term does not include small bodies such as comets, meteoroids, and asteroids, many of which are little more than pieces of ice or rock.

INNER PLANETS

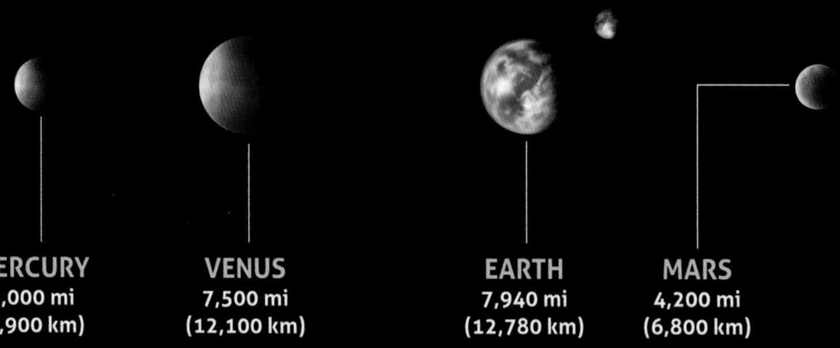

SUN
865,000 mi
(1,392,000 km)

MERCURY
3,000 mi
(4,900 km)

VENUS
7,500 mi
(12,100 km)

EARTH
7,940 mi
(12,780 km)

MARS
4,200 mi
(6,800 km)

Sizes given are the approximate diameter of each body.

INNER AND OUTER PLANETS

The eight planets of the solar system can be divided into two groups—inner planets and outer planets. The four inner planets are Mercury, Venus, Earth, and Mars. These relatively small worlds are composed primarily of rock and metal. The inner planets have solid surfaces. None of these planets has rings, and only Earth and Mars have moons.

The four outer planets are Jupiter, Saturn, Uranus, and Neptune. All of them are much bigger than the inner planets, and Jupiter is more massive than the seven other planets combined. Each of the outer planets also has a ring system and many moons.

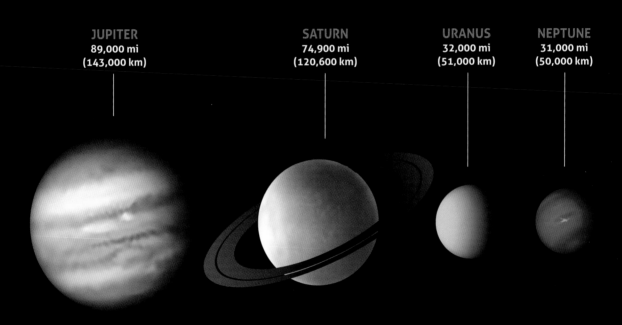

JUPITER	SATURN	URANUS	NEPTUNE
89,000 mi (143,000 km)	74,900 mi (120,600 km)	32,000 mi (51,000 km)	31,000 mi (50,000 km)

OUTER PLANETS

ARE THERE PLANETS OUTSIDE OUR SOLAR SYSTEM?

There are numerous planets in numerous other solar systems.
These planets are called extrasolar planets or exoplanets.

THE SUN

Although the Sun is a rather ordinary star, it is very important to the inhabitants of Earth. The Sun is the source of virtually all Earth's energy. It provides the heat and light that make life on Earth possible. Yet Earth receives only about half a billionth of the energy that leaves the Sun.

WHAT MAKES UP THE SUN?

The Sun is a huge ball of hot gases. Like other stars, it produces enormous amounts of energy by converting hydrogen to helium deep within its interior. More than 90 percent of the Sun's atoms are hydrogen. The Sun has no fixed surface. It is much too hot for matter to exist there as a solid or liquid.

THREE FAST FACTS

1 The Sun contains more than 99 percent of the solar system's mass.

2 The average distance between the Sun and Earth is roughly 93 million miles (150 million kilometers). A ray of sunlight takes only about 8 minutes to reach Earth.

3 The Sun has a surface temperature of about 5,800 K (10,000 °F). It has a core temperature of about 15,000,000 K (27,000,000 °F).

COMPARED TO EARTH

The Sun's diameter is about 864,950 miles (1,392,000 kilometers), which is about 109 times the diameter of Earth. Its volume is about 1,300,000 times Earth's volume. Its mass, or quantity of matter, is some 333,000 times as great as Earth's mass.

← EARTH

SUN

SOLAR WINDS

Spacecraft in interplanetary space have encountered streams of highly energetic charged particles originating from the Sun. These streams, called the solar wind, flow radially outward from the Sun's corona through the solar system and extend beyond the orbits of the planets. These particles are continuously released, but their numbers increase greatly following solar flares and other eruptions.

SOLAR ACTIVITY

The Sun's magnetic activity is quite complex. Rapid, large fluctuations occur in numerous strong local magnetic fields that are threaded through the Sun's atmosphere. Magnetic activity shapes the atmosphere and causes disturbances there called solar activity.

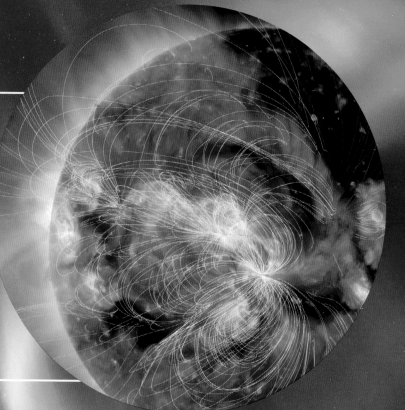

CAN SOLAR ACTIVITY AFFECT THE EARTH?

The Sun's violent eruptions have concrete effects on Earth. Large solar flares and coronal mass ejections shower Earth with streams of high-energy particles that can cause geomagnetic storms. These storms can disrupt communications satellites and radio transmissions and cause surges in power transmission lines. They also create auroras (the northern and southern lights) near the poles.

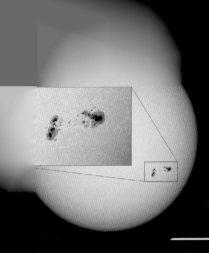

Periodically, darker cooler blotches called sunspots temporarily appear on the Sun's surface. Sunspots are areas where very strong local magnetic fields interfere with the normal convection activity that brings heat to the surface.

SOLAR FLARES

A more violent phenomenon is the solar flare. Flares release magnetic energy that builds up along the boundaries between negative and positive magnetic fields that become twisted.

PROMINENCES

Prominences form along sharp transitions between positive and negative magnetic fields. Early astronomers noticed huge red loops and streamers around the black disk of solar eclipses.

CORONAL MASS EJECTIONS

A type of violent eruption called coronal mass ejections also occurs in the corona. The corona sometimes releases enormous clouds of hot plasma into space.

MERCURY

The planet that orbits closest to the Sun is Mercury. It is also the smallest of the eight planets in the solar system. Relatively little was known about Mercury until the Mariner 10 spacecraft visited it in 1974–75. It was more than 30 years before another spacecraft, Messenger, visited the planet.

The Mariner 10 launch, 1973.

FOUR FAST FACTS

1. Mercury has no known moons.

2. Mercury circles the Sun at an average rate of about 30 miles (48 kilometers) per second, the fastest of the eight planets.

3. The planet was named after the ancient Roman god Mercury, the counterpart of the ancient Greek god Hermes, the swift-footed messenger of the gods.

4. The average surface temperature is about 332° F (167° C).

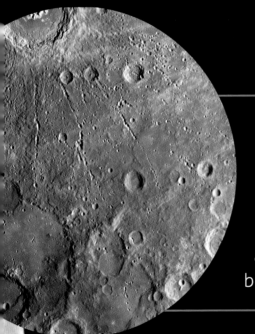

WHAT MAKES UP MERCURY?

Like Earth, Mercury has three separate layers: a metallic core at the center, a middle rocky layer called a mantle, and a thin rocky crust. The core is made mostly of iron. Mercury's surface is dry and rocky. Much of it is heavily cratered. Impact craters form when meteorites, asteroids, or comets crash into a rocky planet or similar body, scarring the surface.

HOT AND COLD

Unlike the other planets, Mercury has no significant atmosphere. Temperatures on Mercury vary widely. Its closeness to the Sun makes it a broiling-hot world by day, with daytime surface temperatures exceeding 800° F (430° C) at parts of the planet. Because Mercury lacks a thick atmosphere to trap heat, however, the planet cools greatly at night. The temperature can drop to about − 300° F (− 180° C) just before dawn.

VENUS

The second planet from the Sun is Venus. After the Moon, Venus is the most brilliant natural object in the nighttime sky. It is the closest planet to Earth, and it is also the most similar to Earth in size, mass, volume, and density.

HOT, HOT, HOT

Venus is always shrouded by a thick layer of clouds. The planet has a massive atmosphere, or surrounding layers of gases, composed mainly of carbon dioxide. This thick atmosphere traps heat, making Venus the hottest planet in the solar system. The planet's average surface temperature is about 867 °F (464 °C), which is hot enough to melt lead.

FOUR FAST FACTS

1. Venus was named after the ancient Roman goddess of love and beauty.

2. Venus has no known moons.

3. Venus was observed from Earth for centuries before the invention of modern astronomical instruments.

4. More than 20 unmanned spacecraft have visited Venus, including craft that have flown by, orbited, and landed on the planet and that have sent probes parachuting through its atmosphere.

INSIDE VENUS

What little is known about Venus's interior is mostly inferred from its similarity to Earth in terms of density and size. Planetary scientists theorize that Venus probably developed an interior roughly like that of Earth, with a metallic core and a rocky mantle and crust.

VOLCANIC VENUS

Venus has a dry, rocky surface. Many of Venus's surface features are associated with volcanic activity. The planet has more than a hundred shield volcanoes, and enormous fields of lava flows cover most of the rolling plains.

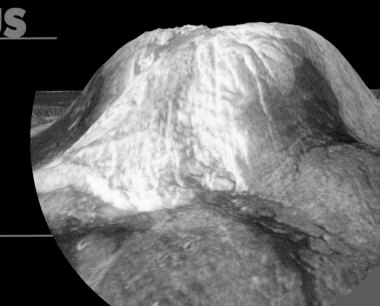

EARTH

The third planet from the Sun is Earth, the home of all known life. While it shares many characteristics with other planets, its physical properties and history allow it to support life in its near-surface environment. In fact, life itself has greatly altered the planet in ways that generally help maintain the conditions for life.

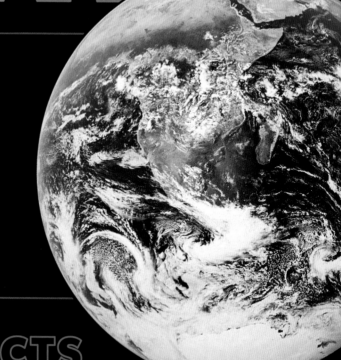

FOUR FAST FACTS

① Water has been cycling since Earth formed. The water in your cup may have been sipped by dinosaurs.

② The circumference at the Equator is 24,902 miles (40,075 kilometers). The diameter at the Equator is 7,926 miles (12,756 kilometers).

③ The deepest well, on the Kola Peninsula in Russia, is about 7.62 miles (12.26 kilometers) deep, reaching only about 1/500 the distance to Earth's center.

④ Earth's inner core contains about 2 percent of Earth's mass. Despite extremely high temperatures, estimated to be between 8,000 and 12,000° F (about 4,400 and 6,600° C), the pressure at the core is so high that the iron and nickel become solid.

EARTH'S SPHERES

Many scientists view Earth as a system composed of interacting smaller systems, called spheres, through which energy flows and matter recycles. The geosphere comprises the inorganic, or nonliving, components of the Earth's system, and can be further divided into three subsystems—the atmosphere (air), hydrosphere (water), and lithosphere (rocks and soil). The biosphere contains the living parts of the system—living organisms and the nonliving factors such as sunlight and water that help supply those organisms with energy and nutrients.

Earth's atmosphere

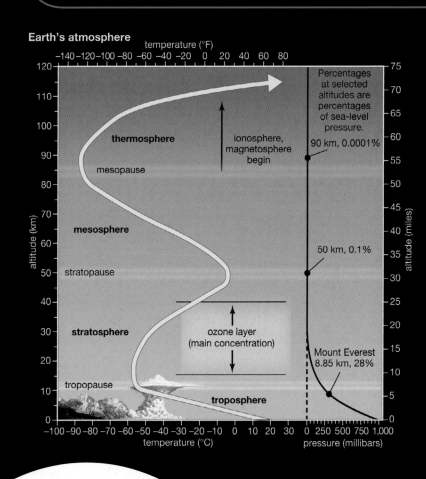

temperature (°F)

thermosphere

ionosphere, magnetosphere begin

mesopause

mesosphere

stratopause

stratosphere

ozone layer (main concentration)

tropopause

troposphere

altitude (km)

altitude (miles)

temperature (°C)

pressure (millibars)

Percentages at selected altitudes are percentages of sea-level pressure.

90 km, 0.0001%

50 km, 0.1%

Mount Everest 8.85 km, 28%

WHAT MAKES UP EARTH?

Earth is largely a ball of rock. The most common atoms present in Earth's rocks are oxygen and silicon, which combine to make silicates such as quartz. Silicates make up about 95 percent of the planet's crust and upper mantle.

EARTH'S MOON

The most prominent feature in the night sky is Earth's natural satellite, the Moon. In astronomical terms the Moon is a fairly ordinary rocky object. Its light is simply reflected sunlight, with dim reflected light from Earth sometimes visible on the part not lit by the Sun.

FOUR FAST FACTS

1. The Italian scientist Galileo Galilei was the first person known to have used a telescope for astronomy, turning one of his own making to the study of the Moon in 1609.

2. The Moon is rather large in comparison to its primary planet, being over a quarter the diameter of Earth.

3. The Moon has almost no atmosphere. Very small amounts of gases such as helium, hydrogen, argon, and neon have been detected.

4. Relatively light-colored and heavily cratered highlands cover about 83 percent of the Moon's surface, while most of the remainder consists of smoother, darker patches—the maria. Nearly all the maria are on the near side.

WHAT MAKES UP THE MOON?

The Moon's surface consists of rocky material, much of it pulverized into dust and other small fragments by billions of years of bombardment by meteorites, large and small. Underneath this is a rocky crust, ranging in thickness from very thin in some areas to over 60 miles (about 100 kilometers) in parts of the Moon's far side. Much of the rest of the Moon is a mantle of semi-molten rock, believed to surround a small, metallic core.

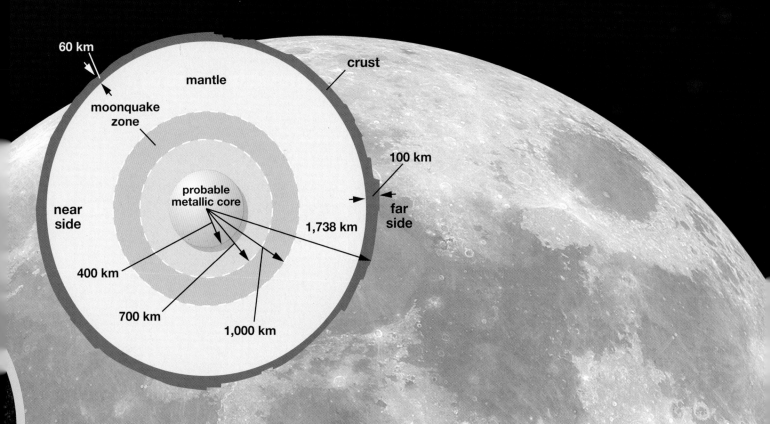

60 km

crust

mantle

moonquake zone

100 km

probable metallic core

near side

far side

1,738 km

400 km

700 km

1,000 km

Explore the Moon with the VR viewer!

MARS

The fourth planet from the Sun is Mars. The planet's surface features include smooth, desolate plains and windblown sand dunes, deep, rugged canyons and steep cliffs, rolling hills, mesas, and enormous volcanoes. Several areas have winding channels that were probably carved by ancient floodwaters.

FOUR FAST FACTS

1 The name Mars is that of the ancient Roman god of war.

2 Mars has two small moons, Phobos and Deimos. Its moons were named for the sons of the Greek god of war, Ares.

3 The rocks and soil on the Martian surface are typically rusty reddish brown because they contain much iron oxide.

Phobos

4 The largest known volcano in the solar system, Olympus Mons reaches a height of 13 miles (21 kilometers) above the average reference altitude (like sea level on Earth). This makes the volcano more than twice as high as Earth's Mount Everest.

WHAT MAKES UP MARS?

The planet's atmosphere is not very dense. Its surface is a cold, dusty desert. Ice caps are found at both the north and south poles. The caps alternately grow and shrink according to seasonal changes.

INSIDE MARS

More than 30 meteorites that have fallen to Earth are known to have come from Mars. The chemical composition of the meteorites indicates that Mars has separated into three main layers like Earth. Earth and Mars both have a metal-rich core at the center; a large, rocky middle layer called the mantle; and an outer crust. Mars's core is probably rich in iron and sulfur.

Several rovers have studied Mars.

JUPITER

The fifth planet from the Sun and the solar system's largest planet by far is Jupiter. The planet is one of the brightest objects in the night sky, and even a small telescope can reveal its multicolored stripes. These stripes are bands of clouds being pushed around the planet by strong east-west winds. Jupiter is a world of complex weather patterns.

FOUR FAST FACTS

1. Jupiter's most prominent feature is an orange-red oval called the Great Red Spot. The spot is a long-lasting storm system that is bigger across than Earth.

2. More than 1,300 Earths would fit inside Jupiter.

3. Jupiter spins very quickly on its axis, faster than the other seven planets.

4. Jupiter has the largest and strongest magnetic field of all the planets.

WHAT MAKES UP JUPITER?

Jupiter has no solid surface. It is formed of the same elements, in roughly the same proportions, as the Sun and other stars. Like Saturn, it is made almost entirely of hydrogen and helium in liquid and gaseous forms.

JUPITER'S RINGS

Jupiter's thin ring system was discovered only by spacecraft, by Voyager 1 in 1979. The rings are composed of tiny dust particles that orbit the planet. The rings are formed of debris produced when small fragments of asteroids, comets, and other objects collide with Jupiter's four small inner moons.

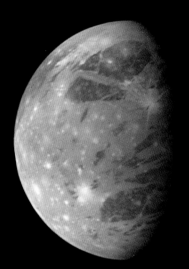

JUPITER'S MOONS

Jupiter reigns at the center of a system of dozens of moons like a miniature solar system. Four of the moons are quite large and would probably be considered planets themselves if they did not orbit a planet: Io, Europa, Ganymede, and Callisto. Io is the most volcanically active body in the solar system. Ganymede, the solar system's largest moon, is bigger than the planet Mercury and has a planet-like magnetic field.

The sixth planet from the Sun is Saturn. Dusty chunks of ice—some the size of a house, others of a grain of sand—make up its extraordinary rings. The other outer planets also have rings, but Saturn's are much larger and more complex. Like Jupiter, Saturn is a giant world formed mainly of hydrogen with no solid surface. It has a massive atmosphere with complex weather patterns.

FOUR FAST FACTS

1 The planet's extensive system of icy moons includes nine major moons and dozens of small ones.

2 Titan, the largest of Saturn's moons, is bigger than the planet Mercury.

3 Titan is the only moon in the solar system known to have a dense atmosphere.

4 It takes Saturn some 29.4 Earth years to complete one revolution around the Sun.

SATURN

SATURN STATISTICS

Saturn is the solar system's second largest and second most massive planet, after Jupiter. The planet is about 95 times as massive as Earth and has more than 750 times its volume. Saturn has the lowest mean density of any of the planets. With only about 70 percent the density of water on average, the planet would float if it could be placed in water.

AROUND SATURN

In spacecraft images of Saturn, the "surface" one sees is mainly clouds. Its hazy appearance is due to the atmosphere above the clouds. Saturn's clouds are formed of molecules of minor compounds that condense in the hydrogen-rich atmosphere.

The Cassini-Huygens probe was launched in 1997.

The Huygens probe being placed in the Cassini orbiter.

SATURN'S RINGS

The main rings have a diameter of about 170,000 miles (270,000 kilometers), and the fainter outer rings extend much farther. The rings are very thin, however, reaching a maximum thickness of roughly 300 feet (100 meters). They are made of countless particles, largely of water ice and dust, all orbiting Saturn like tiny moons.

FOUR FAST FACTS

1 It takes Uranus about 84 Earth years to complete just one trip around the Sun.

2 Uranus has a system of about a dozen narrow rings. Like Saturn's rings, they are made up of countless particles, each orbiting the planet like a small moon. The particles in Uranus' rings are much darker than those found in Saturn's bright, icy rings.

3 Uranus has 27 known moons: five major moons and more than 20 smaller ones.

4 Voyager 2 became the first—and so far only—spacecraft to encounter Uranus, in January 1986, and Neptune, in August 1989.

URANUS

The seventh planet from the Sun is Uranus. It is one of the giant outer planets with no solid surfaces. Although Uranus is not as big as Jupiter or Saturn, more than 60 Earths would fit inside it. The planet is most similar in size and composition to Neptune, its outer neighbor. Like Neptune, Uranus is blue-green because of the small amount of methane in its atmosphere.

A DISCOVERY STORY

Uranus was not known to ancient astronomers. It was seen in early telescopes several times but was thought to be just another star. In 1781, as part of a telescopic survey of the stars, English astronomer William Herschel discovered "a curious either nebulous star or perhaps a comet." This unusual object soon proved to be a planet, the first to be identified in modern times.

THE ATMOSPHERE
Like the other outer planets, Uranus has a massive atmosphere with a composition similar to that of the Sun and other stars. Scientists think it is roughly three quarters hydrogen and a quarter helium by mass, plus a small amount of methane and probably trace amounts of water, ammonia, and other substances.

INSIDE THE PLANET
Scientists think that Uranus is composed mainly of melted ices of water, methane, and ammonia, with some molten silicate rock and metals, and a smaller amount of hydrogen and helium. The interior of Uranus is more like that of Neptune than like the interiors of Jupiter and Saturn, which are mostly hydrogen and helium.

Methane gas frozen in ice on Earth gives it a blue color.

NEPTUNE

The eighth and farthest planet from the Sun is Neptune. It is always more than 2.5 billion miles (4 billion kilometers) from Earth, making it too far to be seen with the unaided eye. It was the second planet, after Uranus, to be discovered through a telescope but the first planet to be found by people specifically searching for one.

FAST FACTS

1 Because of its great distance from the Sun, Neptune takes nearly 165 Earth years to complete one orbit.

2 The dwarf planet Pluto is usually farther from the Sun than Neptune is. About every 248 years, however, Pluto's highly eccentric (elongated) orbit brings it inside Neptune's orbit.

3 Voyager 2 detected considerable atmospheric turbulence during its 1989 flyby. An enormous, whirling, Earth-sized storm system called the Great Dark Spot appeared as a dark oval in photographs of the southern hemisphere. Unlike Jupiter's ancient Great Red Spot, however, Neptune's large storm systems do not seem to be long lasting.

WHAT VOYAGER 2 FOUND

Relatively little was known about the distant planet until the Voyager 2 spacecraft—the only mission to Neptune—flew by it in 1989. The planet that Voyager uncovered is a stormy, windswept world with a vivid blue hue. Neptune has no solid surface. It has a system of rings and more than a dozen moons.

THE ATMOSPHERE

Like the other outer planets, Neptune has a massive atmosphere composed mostly of hydrogen with some helium. Methane makes up most of the rest, accounting for about 2 percent of the molecules within the atmosphere. The methane gives Neptune its bluish color.

INSIDE NEPTUNE

The pressures and temperatures inside Neptune are very high, so the interior is probably liquid. Scientists think it is made mostly of melted ices of water, methane, and ammonia plus molten silicate rock and metal. It also contains a smaller percentage of hydrogen and helium.

DWARF PLANETS

The objects called dwarf planets are similar to the solar system's eight planets but are smaller. The first three objects classified as dwarf planets, in 2006, were Pluto, Eris, and Ceres. Makemake (pronounced "mah-kay mah-kay") and Haumea were named dwarf planets in 2008.

PLUTO

Pluto is the largest member of the Kuiper belt. It is made of ice and rock. Pluto has five moons, four of which are tiny. Its largest moon, Charon, is so large with respect to Pluto that the two are often considered a double-body system. Pluto was considered the solar system's ninth and outermost planet from 1930 until 2006, when it was reclassified as a dwarf planet.

MAKEMAKE

Makemake is reddish in color. Its surface is thought to be covered with frozen methane. Makemake has one known moon. It is named after a creator god in the mythology of the Pacific island of Rapa Nui (Easter Island).

HAUMEA

Haumea is one of the largest known members of the Kuiper belt. It spins on its axis much faster than any other large celestial object, competing one rotation in just under four hours.

ERIS

Eris is on average nearly 68 times farther from the Sun than is Earth, compared with 39.5 times for Pluto.

CERES

The largest known asteroid is Ceres, which lies within the main asteroid belt between the orbits of Mars and Jupiter. It accounts for more than a third of the mass of the entire asteroid belt.

ASTEROIDS

The many small bodies called asteroids are chunks of rock and metal that orbit the Sun. Most are found in the main asteroid belt, a doughnut-shaped zone between the orbits of Mars and Jupiter. Astronomers think that when the solar system was forming, the immense pull of gravity from the object that became Jupiter prevented the asteroids from clumping together to form a planet.

ASTEROID BELT

DISCOVERING ASTEROIDS

The discovery of asteroids dates to 1801, when the Italian astronomer Giuseppi Piazzi observed an object that he later named Ceres. It is the largest known asteroid. Astronomers identified hundreds more asteroids in the 1800s and tens of thousands more in the 1900s. The majority of known asteroids have been discovered since the late 1990s.

Vesta, the largest asteroid after Ceres.

FAST FACTS

1 Only about 30 asteroids are greater than 125 miles (200 kilometers) in diameter. Most are much smaller.

2 There are probably millions of boulder-sized asteroids in the solar system. These small objects likely result from collisions of larger asteroids.

3 The first spacecraft to encounter and photograph an asteroid up close was NASA's unmanned space probe Galileo.

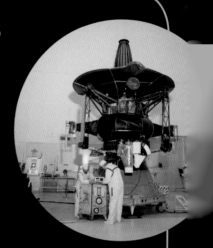

WHEN ASTEROIDS COME TO EARTH

Small asteroids and asteroid fragments regularly strike Earth's surface in the form of meteorites. Much less often, large asteroids crash into Earth, forming huge craters. Past large impacts may have caused earthquakes, giant sea waves, and even global dust clouds that blocked sunlight for long periods.

METEORS AND METEORITES

A flaming streak flashes across the night sky and disappears. On rare occasions the flash of light plunges toward Earth, producing a boom like the thundering of guns and causing a great explosion when it lands. These blazing trails of light are known to be caused by small chunks of stony or metallic matter from outer space that enter the Earth's atmosphere and vaporize.

WHEN METEROIDS COME TO EARTH

Before they encounter Earth's atmosphere, these chunks of matter are called meteoroids. Once they enter the atmosphere, they are called meteors. Most meteors never reach Earth—they are so tiny that they vaporize completely soon after entering the atmosphere. The large, dense objects that do survive the fall to Earth are called meteorites.

THREE FAST FACTS

1 When a meteoroid enters the atmosphere, it is traveling at a tremendous speed—from 1,100 to 5,200 miles (1,800 to 8,400 kilometers) per hour—much faster than the surrounding air.

2 Although thousands of meteoroids enter the atmosphere each year, it is estimated that only about 500 actually reach the ground before vaporizing.

3 On a clear, dark night an observer may see ten or more meteors per hour.

METEORITE CRATERS

When a meteorite of more than 100 tons strikes the ground, it causes a violent explosion. In the explosion, much of the meteorite is blown back out into the atmosphere, and a gaping hole is torn in the ground. There are a number of large craters on the Earth's surface that are known to be the result of meteorite impacts.

See the Moon's craters and find out more about meteors with the VR viewer!

COMETS

A comet is a small chunk of dust and ice that orbits, or travels around, the Sun. When near the Sun, the small bodies called comets develop a hazy cloud of gases and dust. They also often develop long, glowing tails. Most comets originate in the very distant, outer regions of the solar system.

Hale-Bopp

FOUR FAST FACTS

1 Comets can be easily seen from Earth only when they approach the Sun closely. Even then, most are visible only with a telescope.

2 When comets are far from the Sun, they appear in large telescopes as a point of light, like a star.

3 Many people look forward with interest to sighting a comet, but for many centuries comets were believed to have an evil influence on human affairs. In particular, they were thought to foretell plagues, wars, and death.

4 Each time a comet passes close to the Sun, it loses some of its matter. Eventually, the comet may disintegrate, ending up as only a swarm of particles.

EDMOND HALLEY'S WORK

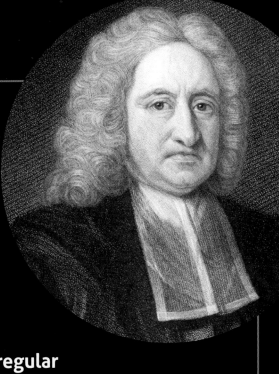

Astronomer Edmond Halley (1656–1742) studied the written accounts of 24 comets that had been seen from 1337 to 1698 and calculated their orbits. He found that the comets of 1531, 1607, and 1682 moved in almost the same paths, and he concluded that they were all the same comet, which would return in about 1758. His forecast was correct. For the first time scientists realized that comets can be regular visitors, and the comet was named after Halley.

STARS

For thousands of years, people have gazed at thousands of stars in the night sky. For most of this time, they could only guess about the nature of these pinpoints of light, often making them objects of wonder, worship, comfort, or fear. More practically, the motions of the stars and planets during the year became the basis for calendars, which were crucial in the development of agriculture. The stars also became valuable tools for navigation. In the last century, scientists determined what stars are—enormous balls of incandescent gas, powered by nuclear fusion reactions in their cores—and that the Sun is one of them.

FOUR FAST FACTS

1 On a clear dark night, far from the artificial lights of a city, one can see as many as 3,000 stars with the unaided eye at a given time.

2 The number of stars in the observable universe (the universe itself perhaps being infinite) is estimated at roughly 10^{22}—about the number of grains of sand on all the beaches of Earth.

3 The brightest star in the night sky is a blue-white star named Sirius. It is also called the Dog Star.

4 Most stars have companion stars, which they mutually orbit. Often, there are just two, so the system is called a double star or binary star.

THE BRIGHTNESS OF STARS

Stars vary considerably in how bright they appear from Earth. Ancient astronomers devised a rating scale for apparent magnitude, or brightness, that is believed to date back to the Greek astronomer Hipparchus in the 2nd century BC. In general, the brighter the star, the lower the magnitude. The scale was useful and has survived (with modifications) to this day.

See constellations with the VR viewer!

HOW STARS SHINE

The vast majority of the energy produced by stars comes from nuclear fusion. Low-mass nuclei (mainly hydrogen) are fused together to make higher-mass (mainly helium) nuclei. Essentially, stars are slow-burning, gigantic hydrogen bombs.

THE COLOR OF STARS

Most people would probably describe stars as "white." However, a careful look shows there are differences. In fact, stars generally lie on a spectrum of color from red, through white, to blue. The physical reason for this is well understood: bluer stars are hotter. In fact, the surface temperature of a star can be accurately determined from a careful analysis of the color. The Sun, which appears almost white, is in between, at 5,800 Kelvin (10,000 °F).

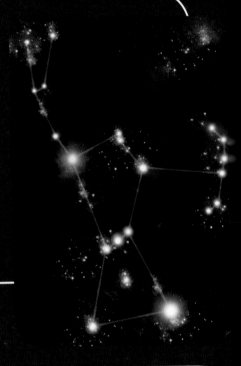

HOW STARS BEGIN

Stars probably begin as clouds of hydrogen and dust. This material slowly pulls itself together into clumps. As the material gets packed in tighter, the clumps get hotter. Pressure builds up. Eventually the star begins changing hydrogen into helium—and so begins to shine brightly.

HOW STARS END

After shining for billions of years, a star uses up all its hydrogen. Small and medium stars slowly cool down and stop shining. This will happen to the Sun billions of years in the future.

Large stars end with a violent explosion called a supernova. After that the material gets crushed much smaller. It no longer shines. Huge stars may end up as objects called black holes. The crushed material is so heavy for its size that it develops a powerful inward pull. This pull, called gravity, is so strong

Mira, a red giant star.

An illustration of a star being eaten by a black hole.

A supernova.

THE SUN'S NEAREST NEIGHBOR

The nearest star to Earth other than the Sun is Proxima Centauri, a dim companion of the brighter pair Alpha Centauri A and B. Proxima Centauri is some 1.29 parsecs (4.2 light-years) from Earth.

cloud of hydrogen and dust condenses

helium core forms as hydrogen shell expands

star finally collapses, forming a white dwarf

main-phase star burns hydrogen in its core (current state of Earth's sun)

star becomes a red giant consisting of a carbon core surrounded by hydrogen envelope

billions of years

TROUBLESHOOTING

The image I see is blurry.

Make sure the smartphone is aligned precisely with the center of the viewer. Adjusting the phone left or right a few millimeters can make a big difference. The tilt of the viewer and the phone can also affect how the screen looks to you. You can also try to calibrate the viewer using one of the QR codes found below.

I was asked to allow the app to take pictures.
Do I need to allow this?

Yes, this allows the app to take a picture of the QR code in your book in order to validate your purchase and access the accompanying app.

How do I calibrate my viewer?

If asked to calibrate your viewer, scan the first of the QR codes found below. If the picture seems blurry afterward, touch the small gear icon that appears at one corner of your screen. You will then be given an opportunity to switch viewers. Scan the other QR code found here. Some smartphones work better with one calibration, while others work better with the second.

I'm getting a pop-up that this app won't work without Google VR Services, asking me to install it before continuing. Do I need to do this?

Click Cancel; it should not prevent you from running the app successfully.

Can I use this viewer with other apps?

The viewer is a standard size that is designed to be compatible with many apps. Try it out!

I damaged my viewer. Can I use this app with other viewers?

Yes, this app is compatible with many other standard-sized viewers on the market.

My screen gets dim when I place it in the viewer.

Check your phone settings. Under Display settings, if there is a setting such as "Auto adjust brightness," where the screen adapts to lighting conditions, turn that setting off.